THE FRIENDLY PHOEBE

The Friendly
PHOEBE

by Berta and
Elmer Hader

THE MACMILLAN COMPANY
NEW YORK   1953

Copyright, 1953, by
BERTA HADER AND ELMER HADER

First Printing

Affectionately dedicated to
Sandra and Julie, two little
chickadees from the south.

THE FRIENDLY PHOEBE

The paper mill whistle sounded the noonday call. Mrs. McGinty picked up her garden tools and basket of weeds. "My Goodness!" she said. "I had no idea it was so late." Mr. McGinty shouldered his rake. He had taken time off from his work to help Mrs. McGinty weed the garden. It was very hot. He mopped his brow and followed Mrs. McGinty. When she reached the stone terrace at the end of the garden she stopped suddenly.

A big crow flew out of the old elm near the house. He flapped his way over the ash trees cawing loudly. He was going somewhere in a hurry. A red squirrel scampered up the roof. He stopped his flight on the ridge and barked angrily. Then he leaped into the apple tree and followed a well remembered path through the branches of the trees to his home in the old oak down in the glen. A black cat ran around the corner of the house. He disappeared down the road. "WHAT'S GOING ON HERE?" exclaimed Mrs. McGinty loudly. Before Mr. McGinty could say a word she held up her hand. "Shhhh," she said. "I hear a baby bird cheeping."

Mr. McGinty leaned the rake he was carrying against the low garden wall. He cupped his hand behind his ear to hear better. Not that his hearing was bad. He claimed he could hear as well as anyone. But he was baffled by the high cheeping cries of baby birds so plainly heard by Mrs. McGinty. He would have thought he was getting hard of hearing but for the fact that Mrs. McGinty couldn't always hear the low thump-thump of the water pump on the hillside below the spring that was music to his ears. He concluded that they lived in different sound worlds. Mrs. McGinty heard the high notes and he heard the low tones. He shook his head. "I can't hear any baby bird cheeping," he said. "Where is it?"

Mrs. McGinty didn't answer. She put down her garden tools and basket of weeds and walked quickly across the terrace. Near the door of the house she stopped and stared at the pavement.

"How in the world did that baby bird get here?" she said. "It is too young to have left the nest."

Mr. McGinty picked up the tiny bird. Its body was covered with a soft, warm, gray down. The short tail feathers were no more than one quarter inch long. Its yellow bill opened and closed in a weak cheeping cry.

"It's a baby phoebe," said Mr. McGinty. "Better look at that nest back of the house. He didn't get here by himself. Something must have . . ."

"Oh dear," interrupted Mrs. McGinty. She hurried into the house. Dozens of tiny mites had left the baby bird and were wandering over Mr. McGinty's hand. He brushed them off and followed Mrs. McGinty to the walled in passageway just in back of the house. A spring tumbled into a basin built in a grotto in the center of the stone retaining wall of the passageway. The water spilled from the basin into a runway that emptied into a drain under the house. Early that spring, the running water and the moss covered stone wall had caught the eye of a passing phoebe. He built a nest of moss and clay just under the eaves in a corner of the house walls. His mate joined him and they started to raise a family.

Mr. and Mrs. McGinty were pleased to have the phoebes in back of the house. Phoebes are insect eaters and help keep the air free of mosquitoes and flies. When Mrs. McGinty climbed the steps from the passageway to the vegetable garden, she could look into the nest. She knew the day the baby phoebes were hatched and she counted the four tiny beaks that cheeped. The mother and father phoebes were busy from dawn to dusk feeding the hungry babies.

"You are right," said Mrs. McGinty sadly. "Something has destroyed the phoebe's nest." She picked up broken bits from the pavement. A small piece of the nest still clung to the wall. "It may have been that crow we just saw or it may have been the red squirrel that scurried over the roof," she said. "Whatever it was must have been frightened and dropped that poor baby on the terrace." She looked all around. There were no signs of the other baby birds, and the mother and father phoebe were gone too. The tiny bird in Mr. McGinty's hand was all alone in a very big world.

"Well, it appears we have an orphan to raise," said Mr. McGinty. "And by the looks of my hand, I had better get some of that powder they dust on canaries, before the mites eat him up." He handed the baby phoebe to Mrs. McGinty.

"I think you had better go to the village right away," said Mrs. McGinty. "Get the powder and buy a medicine dropper too, to feed him with. Hurry back. The poor little thing must be hungry."

While Mr. McGinty was on his errand, Mrs. McGinty lined a small berry basket with a soft piece of cloth and placed the baby phoebe in his new nest. Mrs. McGinty sighed as she looked at the helpless baby bird in the basket. She believed in the divine law of Nature but the law worked in strange ways at times and was not easy to explain. It was a great pity that the phoebe's nest was destroyed but there was no use crying about it now. She went into the kitchen and put an egg on to boil. By the time Mr. McGinty returned from the village the hard-boiled egg was cool. Mrs. McGinty mashed the egg yolk and added a little milk to make a soft mixture. Then she filled the glass dropper with the egg mash.

"Just a minute before you feed him," said Mr. McGinty. He sprinkled a pinch of the canary powder on a bluejay feather he had found on the lawn and dusted the baby bird. The powder worked like magic. The mites disappeared and the little phoebe stopped his restless squirming.

Mrs. McGinty waited patiently until the phoebe opened his beak in a plaintive cry, then she quickly squirted a small quantity of the mash into the open mouth. The baby bird gulped and swallowed. He lay in silent surprise for a moment. Then he opened his beak wide. He wanted more. He was hungry. Mrs. McGinty fed him the mash until his stomach was filled. She smiled as the little phoebe's eyes grew heavy and he tucked his head under his wing and slept.

Whenever the baby bird woke and cheeped, Mrs. McGinty stopped whatever she was doing and fed him. She was pleased to see his eyes grow brighter and his cheep louder. When dusk deepened the shadows in the room, she fed the little phoebe and waited until he tucked his head under his wing. Then she covered the basket with a soft cloth for the night.

Mr. McGinty was up early the next morning. He opened the doors of the house to let in the cool breeze. Then he uncovered the phoebe's basket. "Cheep-cheep-cheep." The baby bird was awake and hungry. Mr. McGinty filled the glass dropper from the cup of fresh mash Mrs. McGinty had stored in the ice chest. He held the baby bird in his hand and fed him slowly. When his hunger was satisfied, the little phoebe nestled in Mr. McGinty's warm hand, tucked his head under his wing and went to sleep. He never wakened when he was put into the cloth-lined basket. He slept most of the day and he kept quiet until he heard voices or footsteps. Then he cheeped steadily until he was fed.

The little phoebe grew fast. Before many days had passed, his downy coat was replaced by feathers. His wings and tail grew longer too. He tried to hop out of the basket and had learned to perch on the edge. Mr. McGinty decided it was time to make a cage. He found a piece of wire mesh that was left over from the fence he had put around the vegetable garden. It was just enough to make a round cage 24 inches high and 18 inches wide. The bottom of the cage was wired on firmly but the top could be lifted off. Mr. McGinty fastened three perches in the cage before he put the phoebe and his basket on the floor of his new home.

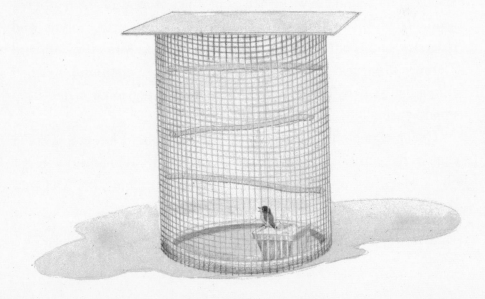

In a few days the baby bird left the basket and hopped happily from perch to perch. Mrs. McGinty took the cage with her when she worked in the garden so the phoebe wouldn't get lonely. He was lively as a cricket now and used his wings as he jumped from perch to perch. He still cheeped loudly for food and only settled down when his stomach was filled. The sun, fresh air and this regular feeding soon turned the ugly fledgling into a plump little phoebe.

Most every summer Mr. and Mrs. McGinty closed the little stone house on Willow Hill for a few weeks while they visited old friends at the seashore. But now a baby bird depended on them. He was too young to travel and he couldn't feed himself. It looked as if they would have to stay home to take care of the phoebe. But one morning as Mrs. McGinty was walking up the road after collecting the mail at the box, she was hailed by her young friend Florence. Florence was a little girl who lived in the city nearby but she often visited her Aunt Mabel, a close neighbor of Mrs. McGinty. Florence always called on her friends in the little stone house on Willow Hill. She liked birds and knew the calls and songs of most of the feathered residents of the hillside. The wood thrush, catbirds, robins and sparrows, and the timid wild doves took flight as Mrs. McGinty and Florence drew near. As they came up the steps, a chipmunk scurried across the garden. They went into the cool living room of the little stone house.

"Cheep-cheep-cheep," called the baby phoebe. Florence saw the cage in the corner. "A BABY BIRD!" she cried. "Where did you get him?" She drew up the small painted Mexican chair Mrs. McGinty kept in the room for young visitors.

Mrs. McGinty told Florence all about how they had found the little phoebe and Florence spent the morning helping Mrs. McGinty feed the baby bird. When she heard that the little orphan would keep her friends from taking their trip to the seashore, she jumped from her chair.

"Please let me have the phoebe while you are away," she said. "I'll take good care of him. I raised a baby robin last summer. Aunt Mabel likes birds and she will help take care of him too."

Mrs. McGinty knew that Florence could be trusted to look after the baby bird. They had planned the trip for a long time. She decided to accept the offer. The day before they closed the little stone house, Mrs. McGinty packed the phoebe's basket with a jar of mashed egg yolk, the canary powder, and the bluejay feather to dust him with. Then she made a gay bouquet of phlox and black-eyed Susans from the garden and tied it to the phoebe's cage with a big yellow ribbon. Mr. McGinty carried the phoebe down the hill to Florence's house.

Florence took good care of the little phoebe. She fed him regularly and carefully covered his basket at night. She carried the cage with her when she went outdoors to sit on the lawn or lie in the swing on the front porch.

One morning when Florence was on the lawn with the phoebe, she took the cover off the cage to straighten one of the perches. The phoebe hopped quickly to her hand and before she realized what was happening, he flew to the upper branches of a tall lilac bush close by. Florence was surprised and scared too! She didn't know the baby bird was old enough to fly. "Fee-bee, fee-bee, come back

here," she cried. What would she say to Mrs. McGinty if the phoebe flew away? Her heart sank at the thought.

"Fee-bee, fee-bee," she called in sweet coaxing tones. He looked at her and chirped an answer but stayed where he was. Florence was in despair. She didn't dare take her eyes off the phoebe for fear he would fly away. Then a housefly buzzed by and lit on her arm. Quick as a wink she hit it. She picked up the fly, but before she could drop it, the phoebe flew to her hand and snapped it up. Though he was just a baby he was a flycatcher. Before he could take off again Florence put him back in the cage. She was so relieved to have the baby bird back she brought out the fly swatter and hunted flies to feed him as a special treat.

By the next week when Mr. and Mrs. McGinty returned from the visit to the seashore and called for the phoebe, Florence had grown very fond of the baby bird. She wanted to take him with her to the city.

"I don't think a phoebe bird would be happy in the city," said Mrs. McGinty. "They like the country with woods and running streams. You can see him whenever you visit your Aunt Mabel. He won't forget you." When Florence told Mr. McGinty how the baby bird liked flies, he got down the fly swatter and added a fly or two to the phoebe's regular meals. They were both surprised to hear that the little phoebe had flown from his cage to the lilac bush. Most young birds took a little more time before they tried out their wings.

"That cage is too small for a bird to fly in," said Mr. McGinty the next morning. "Let's put him in the room where we kept the squirrel. He can really try out his wings there. I'll find something for a perch."

Mr. McGinty found a straggly branch that had fallen from the sycamore onto the road. He brought it to the house and stood it in a corner of the little spare room. The room was light and airy with windows on three sides. Mrs. McGinty took the braided rag rug off the floor and put the chairs in the attic. This left the room quite bare. She called to Mr. McGinty to bring in the phoebe. Mr. McGinty lifted the baby bird out of the cage and placed him on a twig of the sycamore branch. The twig bobbed up and down and the phoebe almost lost his balance. When he righted himself he jumped to another twig. He hopped along the branch from twig to twig. He was pleased with his new freedom and it wasn't long before he began to make short flights about the room.

One morning Mrs. McGinty brought a bucket of water into the phoebe's room to scrub the floor. As soon as she set the bucket down the baby bird flew to the rim chirping excitedly. Mrs. McGinty caught him just as he was about to dive into the water. She remembered then that phoebes love water and build their nests near streams or ponds. She had to put a screen over the bucket to keep the phoebe out of the water while she scrubbed the floor. "Perhaps you would like a bath," said Mrs. McGinty. The baby bird chirped loudly. She filled a saucer with water and placed it on the floor. The little phoebe flew to the edge of the saucer and hopped into the center. He splashed water all over himself and the floor until the saucer was empty. Then he shook his feathers and tried to fly. But he was so wet he couldn't get off the floor. Mrs. McGinty put the little phoebe on a towel in a sunny spot near the window and helped dry him with bits of soft cotton. The baby bird spread his wings in the sun. When every feather was dry he flew to his favorite perch on the sycamore branch.

The little phoebe was growing fast. He was very tame and friendly. Every day he took longer flights about the room. When Mrs. McGinty opened the door of his room to bring him his meal of egg yolk or scraped apple, he flew from his perch to her shoulder and chirped happily. He seemed to be lonesome when left alone, so Mrs. McGinty put him in his cage and carried him about with her when she was doing the daily house chores. When she called "Fee-bee, fee-bee" the baby bird would fly to her hand or shoulder. She left the top off the cage so he could fly freely about wherever she was. Sometimes he perched on the back of a chair or flew to the top of a picture frame hanging on the wall. He liked to sit and watch

Mrs. McGinty from the light fixtures, too. But he always returned to her shoulder to be taken back to his room at the "fee-bee" call.

Mrs. McGinty put the phoebe in his cage and took him with her when she worked in the garden, too. The phoebe did not like to stay in the cage and rubbed most of the feathers off his beak by poking it through the wire mesh. He hopped restlessly from perch to perch in his cage and looked at the trees and shrubs about the garden.

One morning Mr. McGinty placed the phoebe on his finger and said, "You are getting to be a big bird now. I think it is high time you were catching your own food." He walked through the garden with the phoebe clinging tightly to his finger. Bees, flies, and other insects buzzed and hovered around the flowers. Mr. McGinty brought his finger and the phoebe close to a nice fat insect feeding in a bluebell. The baby bird stared at the flower and the trees and sky but he made no move to catch the insect until it took wing. Then he snapped at it but too late.

"Tsk-tsk," said Mr. McGinty. "You missed him. But here's another. Try again." He held the phoebe on his finger and patiently pointed out flies and other small insects but the baby bird did not see them until they took flight or scurried away.

"You will starve to death unless you do better than that," said Mr. McGinty. "Sit here and I'll catch some flies for you." He put the phoebe on a small branch of the wistaria vine that draped over the terrace wall. Then he went indoors to get the fly swatter. The phoebe clung tightly to the vine and watched Mr. McGinty. The phoebe paid no attention to the scolding of the bluejays nor to the warning calls of the other birds perched in the treetops about the garden. The moment Mr. McGinty appeared in the doorway, he spread his wings and flew to the safety of his shoulder and waited to be fed. Mr. McGinty stunned a fly with the swatter, placed it between thumb and forefinger and held it close to the phoebe who quickly snapped it up. Sometimes the phoebe jumped to his hand to get the fly. Mr. McGinty carried the phoebe into the garden every morning, and one day the phoebe caught his first insect on the wing. Mr. McGinty was delighted and the phoebe seemed surprised and happy too. He took off on his first short flights about the garden and began to catch his own food. He always returned to Mrs. McGinty's shoulder when she called from the doorway or to the wistaria vine when he heard the soft thud of the fly swatter. There he would sit and chirp until rewarded by a freshly stunned fly. Then with a flick of his tail he would fly over the garden hedge to perch on a low hanging branch of the mulberry tree. These short flights about the garden were never far from where Mrs. McGinty was working.

One day Mrs. McGinty left the phoebe sitting in the mulberry tree by the terrace while she went to get the pruning shears from the garden tool shed. Just at that moment the bluejays filled the air with warning cries. A young oriole left his perch on a bare branch of the ash tree to seek shelter in the thickly leaved bushes around the garden. He was too late. He was seized in mid-air by a hawk, who dropped like a bullet from the sky and carried him away. Mrs. McGinty had heard the warning of the jays and had seen what happened. She ran across the lawn clapping her hands loudly to drive the hawk away. The little phoebe stared after the big hawk. Like the rest of the birds on the hillside, he too would soon learn what to fear. He flew to Mrs. McGinty's shoulder, and she carried him indoors until the hillside was safe again.

As the days passed the young bird became more adventurous and flew into higher branches of the trees close to the house. One day Mr. McGinty came out of the house with a treat for his friend. He held out his hand and whistled the phoebe call. The bird swooped through the air and plucked the fly from his fingers and returned to his perch in the elm. Mr. McGinty looked at the phoebe in astonishment and admiration. He called to Mrs. McGinty in the garden, "Our phoebe takes his flies on the wing. Watch this now." He held out another fly. Without waiting to be called, the phoebe swooped through the air, plucked his prize and returned to his perch above their heads. Mr. McGinty liked the game and so did the baby bird. He was fast learning the ways of the bird world.

At the end of the day the bedtime twittering of the birds on the hillside told the phoebe that it was time he too returned to his nest. If Mrs. McGinty was working in the garden, he would fly to her shoulder to be carried indoors. Sometimes he flew through the open doorway to perch in his cage. When the house lights were turned on, Mrs. McGinty covered the cage with a cloth. But as the days passed, the phoebe spent less time in his cage. He often flew to the curtain rod above the door to the terrace, where he tucked his head under his wing and went to sleep.

When Mr. McGinty came downstairs in the morning, the phoebe left his perch and flew to his shoulder with a happy chirp. Sometimes he waited to be fed but more often he flew out of the house as soon as the terrace door was opened. He liked to sit in a bush or tree and watch what was happening in the garden.

One morning Mrs. McGinty heard the birds scolding in the tangle back of the butterfly bush. She hurried out of the house thinking the phoebe might be in trouble. The robins and sparrows darted and fluttered angrily in the tangle of vines on the slope just outside the garden. She walked around the butterfly bush. The phoebe was nowhere to be seen, but what Mrs. McGinty did see made her open

her eyes wide in astonishment. "My Goodness," she exclaimed. She ran back to the house. "Bring the ladder quick," she called to Mr. McGinty. "A poor little screech owl has caught his foot in the honeysuckle tangle and is hanging upside down. Hurry before the birds peck his eyes out." Mr. McGinty fetched the ladder.

The owl hung motionless with his back against a small locust tree a short distance above Mr. McGinty's head. He opened his sharp beak when the birds darted at him and he blinked his fierce yellow eyes and stared when Mr. McGinty placed the ladder against the tree.

"Be careful," warned Mrs. McGinty as Mr. McGinty climbed the ladder. "He may bite you." As Mr. McGinty reached out to free the owl, the ladder slipped. He saved himself from a fall by grabbing the trunk of the tree. "Oh dear! I told you to be careful," said Mrs. McGinty as she moved quickly to steady the ladder. Suddenly, to the great astonishment of Mr. and Mrs. McGinty, the owl let go his hold on the vine, spread his wings and flew away followed by the scolding birds!

"Well!" said Mrs. McGinty. "What do you know about that? He wasn't caught at all. He was just playing possum. He must have been after a bird. Oh dear." She looked hurriedly around the garden and called "Fee-bee, fee-bee." To her great relief the phoebe flew out from his hiding place in the bush and landed on her shoulder.

While Mr. McGinty put the ladder away, Mrs. McGinty arranged some flowers on the breakfast table on the terrace. As Mrs. McGinty poured the coffee, the little phoebe dropped to perch on a stalk in the bouquet. He joined in the conversation from time to time with a cheerful chirp. Sometimes bluejays perched in the trees near the terrace and stared at the phoebe visiting with his friends at the breakfast table. Their warning cries did not frighten the phoebe, nor was he bothered by the scolding of the wren from his house in the witch hazel tree nearby. He flew away from time to time to catch a fly but he always returned before breakfast was finished and the table taken away.

Though he was growing every day, he was still a baby bird and never went far from home. He seemed quite content with his foster parents and he paid little attention to the distant call of the phoebes who lived in the glen at the foot of the old quarry. He flew freely in and out of the house. When Mr. McGinty played a merry tune on the piano, he sat on his shoulder or flew to his hand and rode up and down the keyboard. Mr. McGinty thought it was fun and the phoebe seemed to enjoy the ride too.

One morning when the phoebe was sitting on Mr. McGinty's shoulder watching him play the piano, Florence came into the room with a young friend, Joan. Joan's eyes opened wide and she pointed her finger at the bird on Mr. McGinty's shoulder. "Birdie-birdie," she said. The phoebe chirped a greeting and flew to Joan's out-stretched finger. Joan was too astonished to move. Then with a flick of his tail, the friendly little phoebe flew out the open window to perch on the wistaria vine. Joan ran out of the room onto the terrace. "Birdie-birdie," she called again and held out her hand. To her delight the phoebe flew to her finger. Every day the two little girls came up the hill to see the phoebe until they had to return to the city.

As the days passed the phoebe's curiosity led him to make longer flights about the garden and one afternoon he found the goldfish pool near Mr. McGinty's work room. Only the bluejay perched in the wild cherry tree near the pool saw what happened next. And his cry of alarm woke the hillside. The robins on the lawn stopped hunting worms and ran toward the pool. Mrs. McGinty stopped her weeding at the call of the jay. She knew the warning cry meant trouble somewhere. Her sharp ears had heard a splash in the pool and she hurried across the lawn after the robins. And she found the trouble. She yelled to Mr. McGinty.

"Hurry-hurry. The phoebe is in the pool. Come quickly or he will drown." Mr. McGinty dropped his work and hurried to the pool.

The baby bird was flapping his wings and splashing about but he could not rise from the water. Mr. McGinty waded into the center of the pool and scooped him up. The poor little phoebe was wet and frightened. He gasped for breath and Mr. McGinty thought he was dying as he carried him into the house and placed him on a towel to dry.

"Fill the hot water bottle," said Mrs. McGinty. "The poor little thing is cold. He may get pneumonia."

Mr. McGinty filled the hot water bottle and put it under the towel. The baby bird lay quietly on the warm towel. He opened his beak from time to time but made no sound. After awhile he spread his wings and began to preen his feathers. Mrs. McGinty was relieved. The phoebe was dry in about an hour and Mrs. McGinty placed him in his basket in the cage. He chirped for food but he was content to stay indoors the rest of that day.

The little phoebe seemed to have forgotten about his unhappy dip in the pool by the next morning and when he was taken outdoors he flew about the garden as usual. He flew to a low hanging branch of the apple tree that reached over the pool. Mrs. McGinty saw him sitting there. "Oh dear!" she said. "He hasn't learned his lesson. He'll be in the water again and he'll drown unless we watch him every minute." What to do next? Mrs. McGinty thought quickly. Then she called Mr. McGinty. "Bring that roll of mosquito netting stored in the attic. We'll have to cover the goldfish pool while the phoebe is in the garden."

And so the pool was covered. The baby bird could no longer get into the water and he was safe.

A few days later the phoebe ventured away from the garden for the first time. He flew to one of the topmost branches of the tall ash tree that grew on the hillside in front of the house. From this high point, the baby bird could see the little waterfall that tumbled down the steep rocky slope of Willow Hill into a dark pool below. With a chirp and a flick of his tail, he dove from his high perch, skimmed over the top of the dogwood and came to rest on a branch of a young birch tree that reached over the new pool. The spray from the falling water wet him and he hopped farther away. There were fish in this pool too, and the air above the water was full of flying insects. It was a perfect place for a phoebe and he stayed there all afternoon. The noise of the water tumbling on the rocks drowned out Mrs. McGinty's voice when she called "Fee-bee, fee-bee" from the terrace above, and the dusk of evening had settled on the hillside before the phoebe took wing for home. He followed a passing ruby throated hummingbird back to the Beauty Bush in the garden.

When Mr. McGinty whistled the "fee-bee" call from the doorway of the house, he flew to his hand. He had been catching insects all afternoon and when he flew back to the house he was too full to eat the fly Mr. McGinty offered him. He tucked his head under his wing and went to sleep on a branch of the apple tree.

After the evening meal, Mr. and Mrs. McGinty came out of the house to sit on the terrace. There they could keep an eye on the sleeping phoebe and forget the little troubles of daily life as they watched the moon rise and listened to the night songs of the katydids and the crickets.

Mr. and Mrs. McGinty sat in silence under the magic spell cast by the moon on the hillside. They found happiness and contentment in the tiny piece of the world they shared with the insects and wild creatures of Willow Hill. When the moon was high in the sky and bathed the hill in a silvery light, they knew the hour was late, though a ruby throated hummingbird was still up sipping the honey hidden in the scarlet petunias that grew in the garden border at the edge of the terrace. They looked at the little phoebe sleeping peacefully and decided not to waken him when they went indoors.

The little phoebe was up and about when Mr. McGinty opened the door the next morning and chirped a greeting from the wistaria vine. He seemed undisturbed by his first night out but he flew indoors at the close of the day to spend the night on the curtain rod above the door.

Every day now the phoebe flew down to the pool below the waterfall but he usually returned in the evening to spend the night in the house with his friends.

One day when he was sitting on his favorite perch above the pool, the sun went under a great black cloud. The long dry spell of the summer was coming to a close and there was a smell of rain in the cool air that drifted down the slope of Willow Hill. Then a high wind brushed the tops of the trees and shook the leaves. The wind grew stronger and the young trees bent and swayed. The rush of the wind through the trees could be heard above the splash of the waterfall. The phoebe was having a wonderful time catching insects and paid no attention to the gathering storm. The rumble of thunder heard faintly in the distance drew closer and grew louder, much louder. The noise of the waterfall, the roar of the wind through the trees and the rumble of thunder drowned out Mr. McGinty's whistle and Mrs. McGinty's "fee-bee" call from above. If the little phoebe had been older and wiser he would have noticed that all the birds of Willow Hill had taken to cover but he had never seen a storm. Suddenly there was a flash of lightning followed by a clap of thunder that shook the hillside and the rain came. Then the phoebe sought shelter but it was too late. Maybe he hadn't been

eating the right kind of food to make his feathered coat oily enough to shed the rain, for in a few moments the poor little phoebe was so wet he couldn't fly. He hopped along the swaying branch to the rocky steep hillside and began the slow climb to safety. He hopped from ledge to ledge until he reached the garden terrace. There he met the full force of the wind and was swept across the flagstones. He was stopped by a pile of wet leaves that had been blown against the low garden wall under the apple tree. He lay there terrified.

Inside the little stone house on the hill, Mrs. McGinty stared out of the window into the storm. She was worried and wondered what could have happened to the little phoebe. She saw some leaves swept by the high wind across the terrace. One of the leaves seemed

to be running! It came to rest under the apple tree. A running leaf?
Mrs. McGinty knew that leaves didn't run. She put a shawl over her
head and ran out into the heavy downpour to the apple tree. At
first glance she saw only the leaves. Then she saw the running leaf.
IT WAS THE LITTLE PHOEBE! The poor little bird was so wet
his head seemed bald and his tail was like a string. He looked more
like a strange insect than a bird. He lay limp and shivering on the
leaves. Mrs. McGinty picked him up and ran back to the house.
The poor phoebe's chirp was just a squeak and he trembled as
though having a chill. Again he was placed on a towel warmed by
the hot water bottle and Mrs. McGinty helped dry his feathers
with soft bits of cotton.

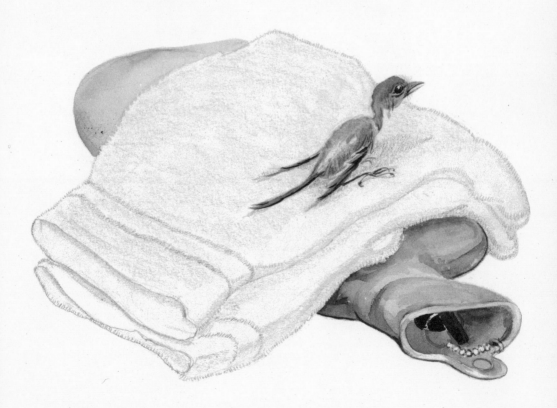

After he had rested for some time he began to take an interest in life again. He stayed in Mrs. McGinty's lap for a couple of hours while he was getting dry. He stood up from time to time to stretch his wings and preen his feathers. When he was quite dry he flew to his roost on the curtain pole to sleep. He slept through the crashing thunder and flashes of lightning that lit the room and didn't waken until Mr. McGinty opened the doors the next morning.

The sun shone brightly and the air was sweet smelling and fresh after the rain. Mrs. McGinty walked slowly through the garden with the phoebe perched contentedly on her shoulder. He was ready for fresh adventures.

The warm summer days were passing rapidly by. The phoebe visited the pool below the waterfall every day but at the first sign of rain he returned to the house. He began to be more adventurous and took longer flights over the treetops but always within hearing distance of a whistle or call. Some days it was well after sundown before he returned, so Mr. McGinty built a small house for him and attached it to the stone wall of the house just under the eaves near the terrace door. It was a pretty house but the phoebe never went near it. At dusk he would perch in the wistaria vine and wait patiently to be let in the house. After a short visit with his friends he would fly to his favorite perch on the curtain rod and go to sleep. As soon as Mr. McGinty opened the door in the morning he flew out of the house to catch his breakfast down by the pool. Then he was off on a new adventure somewhere on the hillside.

As the days grew shorter his flights seemed to grow longer. Some days the phoebe went away in the morning and there was no answering chirp to Mr. McGinty's whistle or Mrs. McGinty's call until sundown. And there came days when he didn't return at all but stayed out all night. Though she wanted the phoebe to have his freedom, Mrs. McGinty always worried when night fell on the hill and the phoebe hadn't returned.

"Something must have happened to the phoebe," she would say to Mr. McGinty. "He ought to be home at sundown."

"Oh, he is all right," Mr. McGinty would assure her. "He's full grown now and is making up for lost time in the bird world. His instinct tells him that phoebes fly south for the winter and he is probably looking for a friend to show him the way."

But most of the time, the friendly little phoebe returned from his wanderings when the shadows of evening fell over the hillside. He perched on a chair near the table and visited while they ate their supper. Then he flew to the curtain rod to sleep.

The autumn nights turned cool and the air was fragrant with woodsmoke from many chimneys. Most of the garden flowers had faded or gone to seed. The flagstones of the terrace in front of the house were prettily spotted with the scarlet leaves of the maple that grew near the door. The green leaves of the ash trees were turning yellow and the big leaves of the whitewood were spotted with gold. The oriole's song was no longer heard on the hillside and the catbirds, robins, song sparrows and thrushes had left Willow Hill for their winter home in the south. And Mrs. McGinty couldn't help worrying about their little phoebe. They seemed to be his only friends. She had never seen him with other birds. She heard the call of other phoebes from afar and she hoped their little phoebe had made friends with them on his flights away from the house. She felt that he would need help to find his way to a winter home in

the southlands. The phoebe still returned at dusk and chirped on the terrace but he spent most of his nights in a sheltered bush or tree near the house. He lived more and more in a bird world.

It was about this time that Florence climbed the winding dirt road up Willow Hill one afternoon. She was leaving that day for the winter in the city and had come to say good-bye to her friends and the little phoebe. But the little bird was nowhere to be seen and there was no answering chirp to Mrs. McGinty's call. Black headed little chickadees and snowbirds hunted for seeds in the garden and a cardinal flew around the corner of the house on the way to the feeding station on the wall, but there was no sign of the little gray phoebe. Mr. McGinty joined them on the terrace, and he too, whistled but there was no answer. They took turns whistling and calling and they waited and watched and listened. They no longer heard even the distant call of the phoebes in the glen.

"Well," said Mr. McGinty, "I guess our little friend is on his way to the sunny south. He's a smart bird. When winter comes rolling around, he'll be singing in the sunshine while I'm shoveling snow."

"Wait," said Florence pointing into the sky. "That looks like a phoebe."

A small bird flew over the tops of the trees back of the house. It landed on one of the uppermost branches of the whitewood. Could it be the phoebe? Florence whistled "Fee-bee, fee-bee." The bird chirped in answer and flicked his tail. IT WAS THE PHOEBE. He swooped down to Florence's shoulder and chirped in her ear. He flew to Mr. McGinty's shoulder and chirped some more. Then he jumped to Mrs. McGinty's shoulder still chirping sweetly. Florence was all smiles. Mrs. McGinty was happy and Mr. McGinty smiled too. Their little phoebe had come home. But not to stay. As Mrs. McGinty turned to take him into the house, he chirped again and for the first time gave the phoebe call, "Fee-bee, fee-bee." Then with a flip of his tail, he took off in the direction from which he had come. He had just returned to say good-bye. They watched until he disappeared into the deepening gold of the sunset sky. The stone house on the hillside would seem very quiet without the sweet chirping of their little friend. They all wished him well on his new adventure. They would miss the friendly little phoebe but they knew they would see him again when the summer birds returned to Willow Hill in the spring.

—— The End ——

HADER BOOKS

BIG CITY

THE BIG SNOW

COCK-A-DOODLE-DOO

FARMER IN THE DELL

THE FRIENDLY PHOEBE

LITTLE APPALOOSA

THE LITTLE STONE HOUSE

LITTLE TOWN

LITTLE WHITE FOOT

LOST IN THE ZOO

MIDGET AND BRIDGET

THE MIGHTY HUNTER

PANCHO

RAINBOW'S END

THE SKYROCKET

SPUNKY, A SHETLAND PONY

SQUIRRELY

TOMMY THATCHER GOES TO SEA